Pre-K

Hooked on Math®

Numbers

Designed and illustrated by
Big Yellow Taxi, Inc.

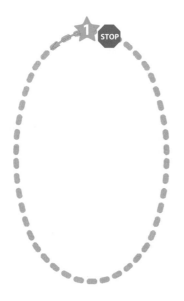

Trace, then write the number 0.

Looking for 0

Circle each 0 you see in the picture.

How many aliens do you see?
Circle your answer.   0   1   2

Hooked on Math *Numbers*

1

Trace, then write the number 1.

Color the Door

Color the door with a 1 on it red.

How many red doors do you see?   1   2   3

Hooked on Math *Numbers*

2

Trace, then write the number 2.

2   2

2   2

Pick a Path

Trace the path that takes Pop Fox to his alien friends.

How many aliens do you see?   1   2   3

Hooked on Math *Numbers*

3

Trace, then write the number 3.

3 3

3 3

Toy Time

Color the toy with a 3 on it yellow.

How many toys do you see?   1   2   3

© 2006 HOP, LLC

Hooked on Math *Numbers*

Act It Out

Toss a coin onto these two pages.
What number did it land on?
Jump, turn, or clap that many times.

1
Jump

2
Turn

3
Clap

Hooked on Math *Numbers*

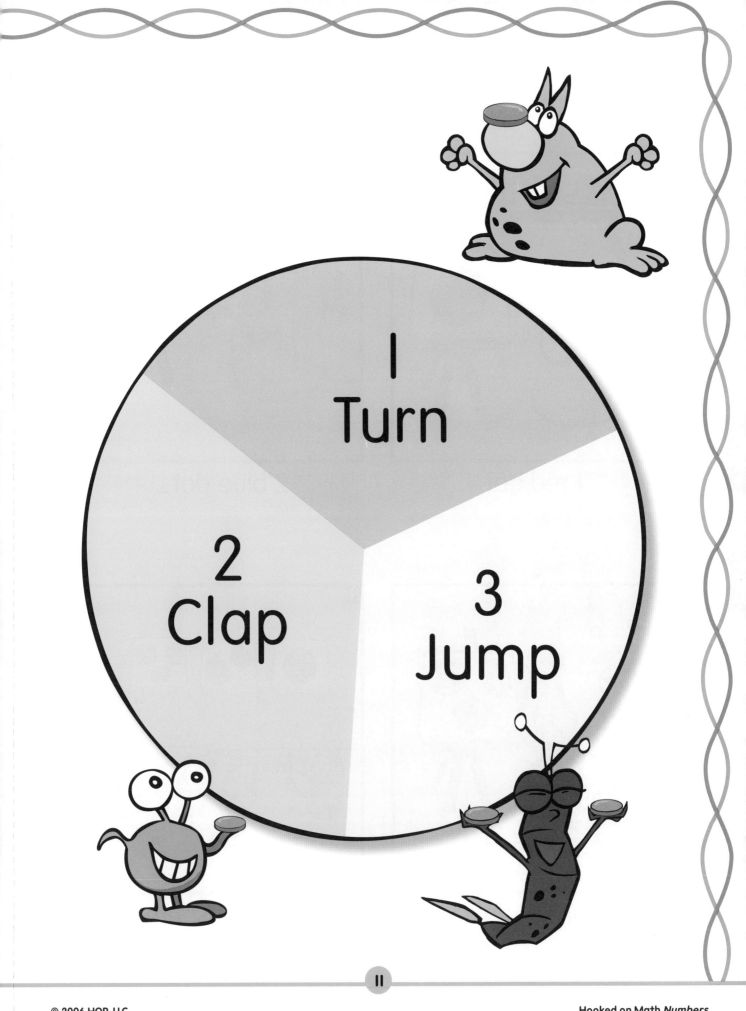

Hooked on Math *Numbers*

A Work of Art

I red dot.

2 blue dots.

3 green dots.

I art museum.

Find the Alien

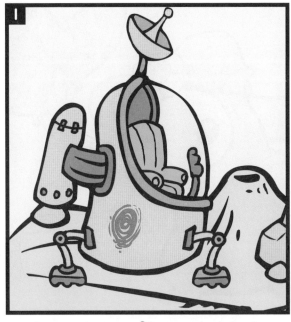

I orange fingerprint.

2 orange fingerprints.

3 orange fingerprints.

I orange alien.

Hooked on Math *Numbers*

Trace, then write the number 4.

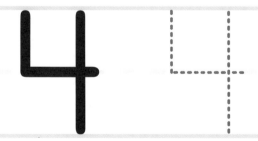

Building Blocks

Help the aliens build their house.
Color each block that has a 4 on it blue.

How many blue blocks do you see?   3   4   5

Hooked on Math *Numbers*

5

Trace, then write the number 5.

5 5

5 5

Hooked on Math *Numbers*

Puzzle Match

Draw lines to match the pieces to the puzzle.

How many puzzle pieces do you see?   5   6   7

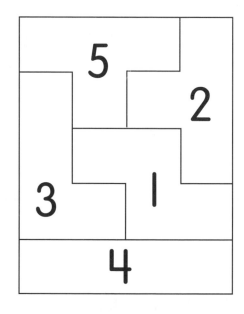

5

2

3

1

4

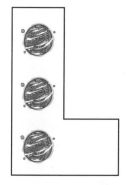

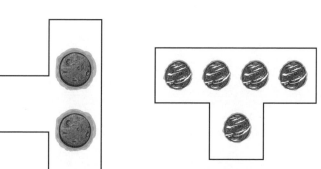

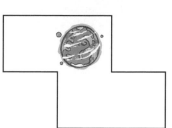

17

6

Trace, then write the number 6.

6   6

6   6

Find the Balloon

Follow the string and find the alien's balloon.
Say the number on his balloon out loud.

How many balloons do you see?   4   5   6

Hooked on Math *Numbers*

7

Trace, then write the number 7.

7

7

Pick a Path

Get the alien to the spaceship.
Draw a path through the squares with a 7 on them.

How many squares
are on the path?　　7　　8　　9

6	6	6	6	7	5
6		7	7	7	5
6	7	7			5
	7			5	5

21

Star Match

Draw lines to match the pieces to each puzzle.

Hooked on Math *Numbers*

What's That Number?

There are numbers everywhere.

Look for the numbers 1 to 7 around your home.

Make a list of things with each number.

Count all the things on the list.

Note to Parents
Calendars, clocks, remote controls, and measuring cups all offer children opportunities to count and read numbers. Talk with your child about the ways that you use numbers every day and encourage him to help, for example, setting the timer when cooking or finding your favorite music track on a CD.

Search for numbers outside of your home.

Look for numbers on price tags, on the dashboard of your car, on road signs, and anywhere else you can find them.

Then play a counting game and look for the numbers 1 to 7 in order.

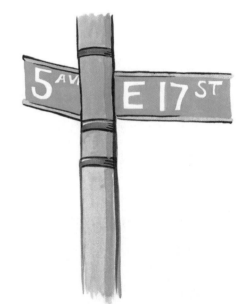

8

Trace, then write the number 8.

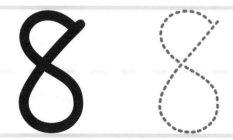

Star Count

Count the stars.
Color the kite with the matching number green.

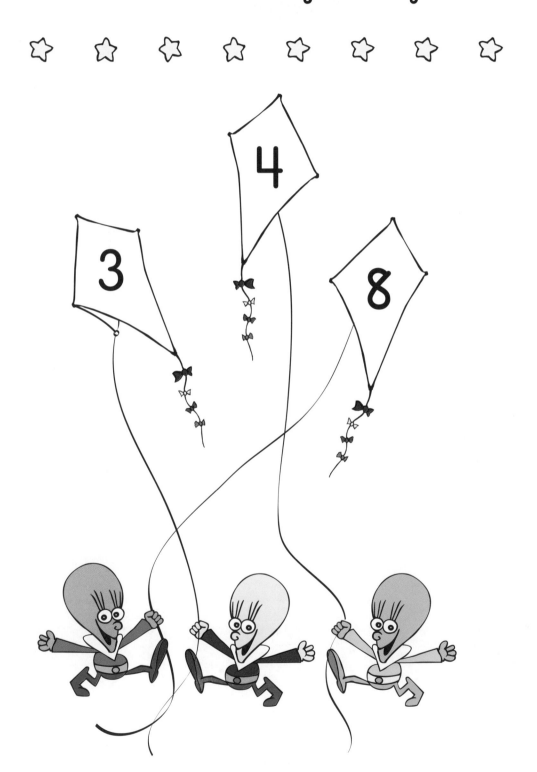

9

STOP

Trace, then write the number 9.

9　9

9　9

Connect the Dots

What is the alien doing? Connect the dots from 1 to 9.

How many worms do you see?   7   8   9

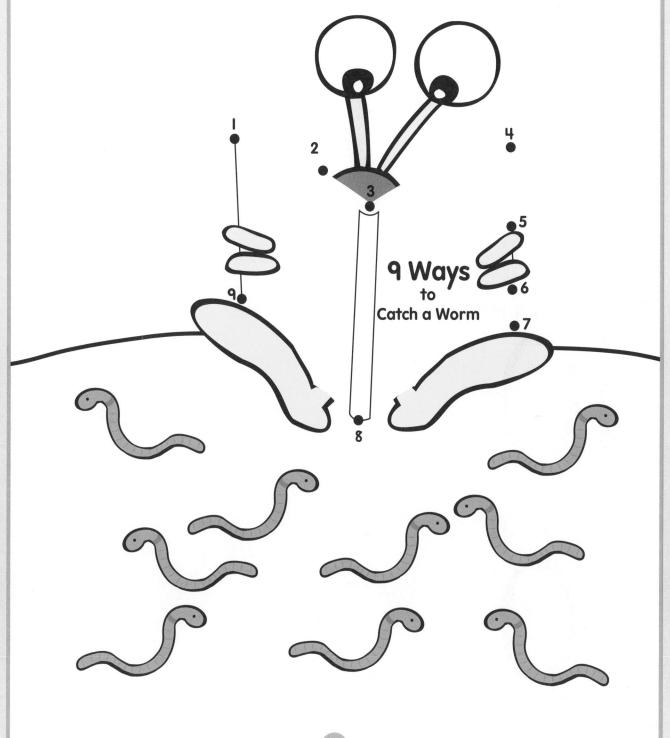

9 Ways
to
Catch a Worm

© 2006 HOP, LLC

Hooked on Math *Numbers*

Trace, then write the number 10.

10 |0

10 |0

Boot Match

Draw a line from the alien to her missing boot.

How many boots do you see?   8   9   10

Hooked on Math *Numbers*

11

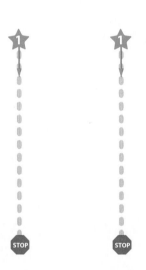

Trace, then write the number 11.

Hooked on Math *Numbers*

Find the Flag

Color the flag with an 11 on it purple.

How many flags do you see?   10   11   12

Hooked on Math *Numbers*

8 and 9 Are Fine

Circle the groups that have 8 things.
Put an X on the groups that have 9 things.

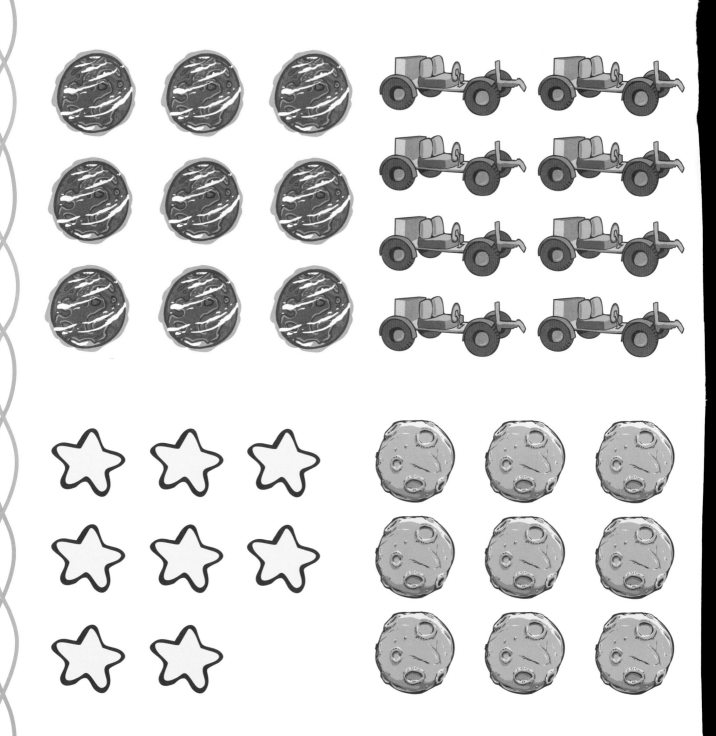

10 and 11 Again

How many spaceships do you see?   10   11

How many aliens do you see?   10   11

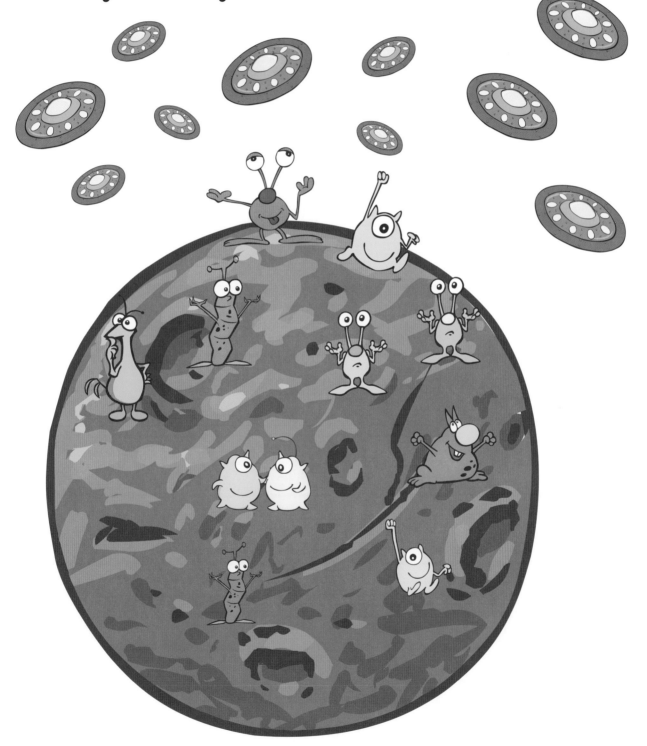

Hooked on Math *Numbers*

Alien Hopscotch

1

8 hops.

2

9 hops.

3

10 hops.

4

11 feet. 0 hops.

Alien Playground

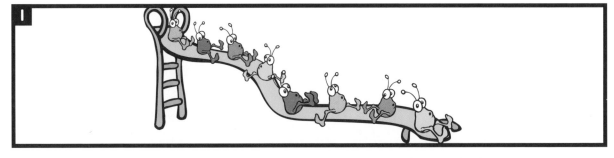

How many aliens are on the slide?

How many aliens are on the swings?

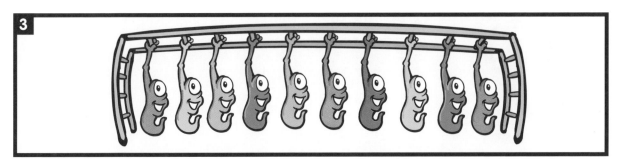

How many aliens are on the monkey bars?

How many aliens have to go home?

Hooked on Math *Numbers*

Trace, then write the number 12.

12 12

12 12

Find the Triangle

Color the triangle with a 12 on it blue.

How many triangles do you see?   12   13   14

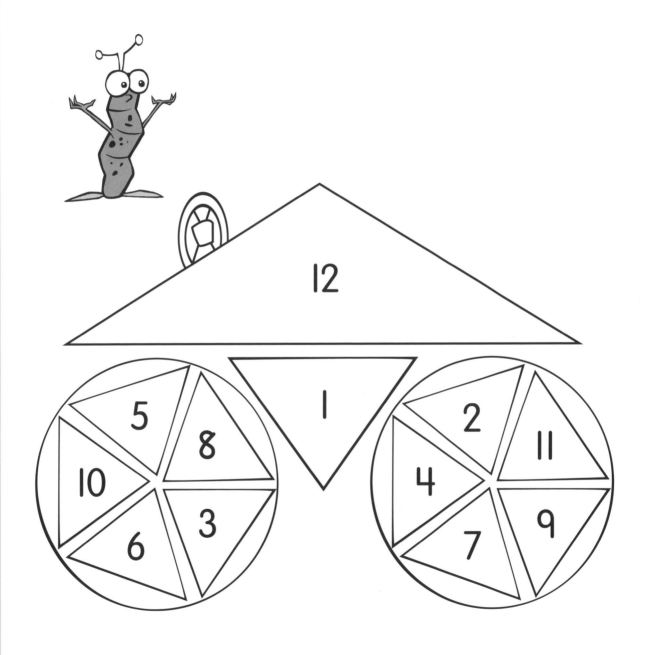

39

Trace, then write the number 13.

13 | 13

13 | 13

Find the Telescope

Color the telescope with a 13 on it green.

How many telescopes do you see?   11   12   13

41

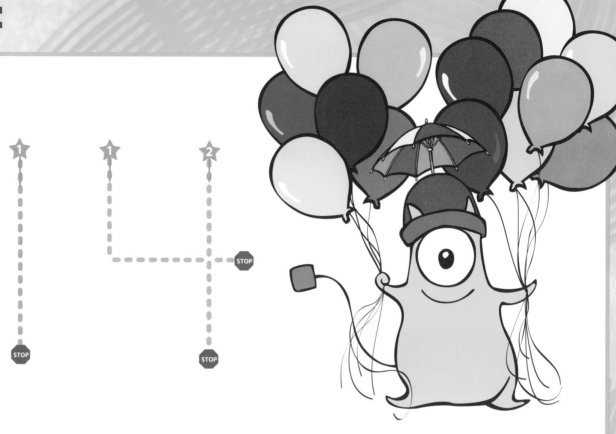

Trace, then write the number 14.

14 14 14

14 14 14

Count the Candles

Help the alien blow out the candles and make a wish.

How many candles do you see?   14   15   16

43

15

Trace, then write the number 15.

15 15

15 15

Hooked on Math *Numbers*

Connect the Dots

What did the alien lose? Connect the dots to find out.

How many space fruit do you see?   14   15   16

© 2006 HOP, LLC

Hooked on Math *Numbers*

Act It Out

Choose any square. Circle the number of spots.
Then pretend to be that creature.

12   13   14   12   13   14

13   14   15   13   14   15

12 13 14   12 13 14

13 14 15   13 14 15

Hooked on Math *Numbers*

Number Song

Create a family song.

Gather all the musical instruments you can find. Look for plastic containers, paper tubes, hands, feet, voices, and anything else you can find that makes noise.

Give one or more instruments to each person.

Then sit in a circle.

Note to Parents
You can do this activity using your hands, feet, voices, banging on a pot or pan, or anything that makes a happy noise.

The first person plays 1 note or beat, such as a stomp, clap, or la-la-la, on his instrument.

Going around the circle, each person adds a note, so that the second person plays or sings 2 notes, the third person 3 notes, and so on.

Say each number before you play it.

Keep playing until someone plays 15 notes. Then take turns playing, stomping, clapping, or singing a certain number of notes.

Everyone else must listen and count, and then play the same number of notes.

Note to Parents
For an easier variation of this game, the first time around each person plays 1 note. The second time around, each person plays 2 notes, and so on.

16

Trace, then write the number 16.

16 6

16 6

Hooked on Math *Numbers*

Pick a Path

Take the alien to her family.
Draw a path through 16 planets of the same color.

How many alien eyes do you see?   15   14   16

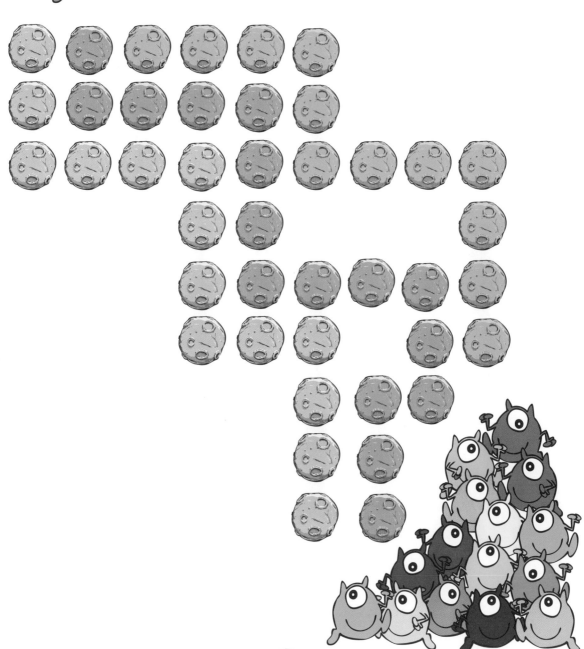

Hooked on Math *Numbers*

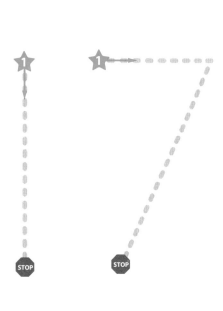

Trace, then write the number 17.

Hooked on Math *Numbers*

Alien Count

Count the aliens in each group.
Circle the group that has 17 aliens.

53

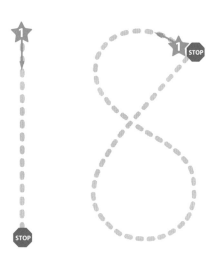

Trace, then write the number 18.

Helmet Match

Pop Fox is looking for his helmet.
Circle the helmet with an 18 on it.

How many helmets do you see?   16   17   18

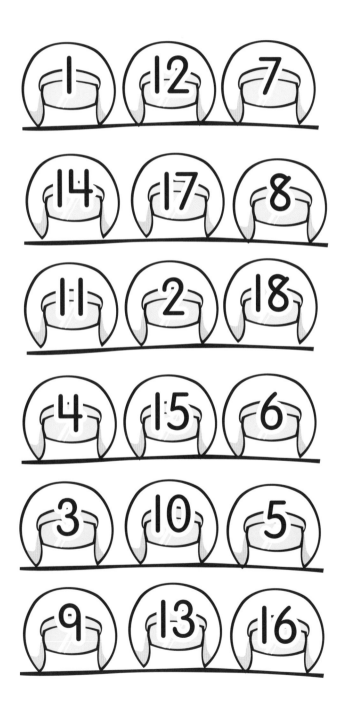

55

19

Trace, then write the number 19.

19   ⁹

19   ⁹

Hooked on Math *Numbers*

Star Maze

I did it!

Draw a path to get the aliens back to their ship.

How many shooting stars do you see?   18   19   20

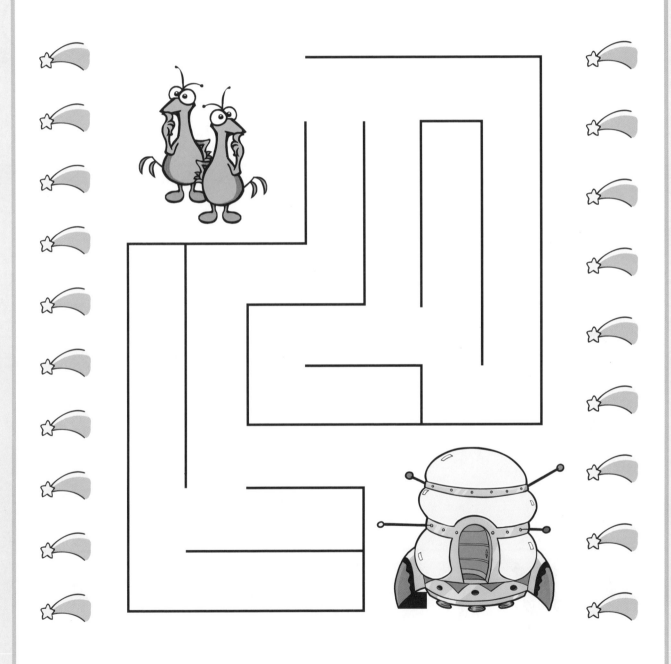

Hooked on Math *Numbers*

Trace, then write the number 20.

20 20

20 20

Meteor Match

Color the meteor with a 20 on it orange.

How many meteors do you see?   18   19   20

© 2006 HOP, LLC

20 Numbers

Trace the numbers from 1 to 20.

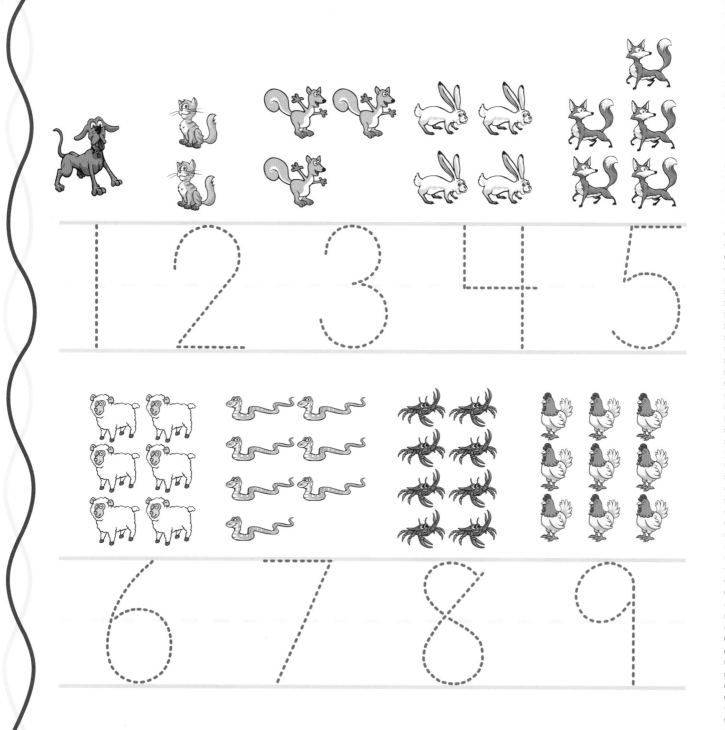

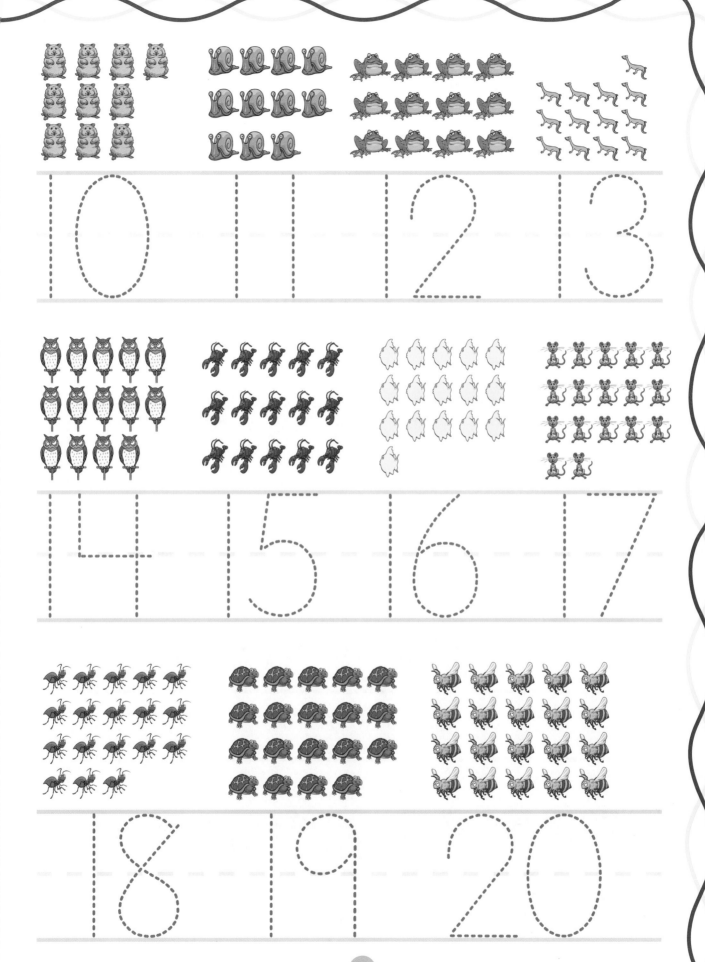

10 11 12 13

14 15 16 17

18 19 20

Hooked on Math *Numbers*

Line Up

That's not right!

That's right!

That's not right!

That's right!

5

That's not right!

6

That's right!

7

That's not right!

8

That's right!

Hooked on Math *Numbers*

I did it!

Congratulations!

_____

has successfully completed this workbook.